First published in Great Britain 2024 by Farshore
An imprint of HarperCollins*Publishers*,
1 London Bridge Street, London SE1 9GF
www.farshore.co.uk

HarperCollins*Publishers*
Macken House, 39/40 Mayor Street Upper, Dublin 1, D01 C9W8, Ireland

Written by Laura Jackson.

© 2024 Disney Enterprises, Inc.

ISBN 978 0 0086 1689 2
Printed and bound in Romania
001

A CIP catalogue record for this title is available from the British Library.

Parental guidance is advised for all craft and colouring activities. Always ask an adult to help when using glue, paint and scissors. Wear protective clothing and cover surfaces to avoid staining.

Stay safe online. Farshore is not responsible for content hosted by third parties.

FSC	MIX
www.fsc.org	Paper | Supporting responsible forestry
	FSC™ C007454

This Disney

FROZEN

Annual 2025

Belongs to . . . .

. . . .

Age . . . .

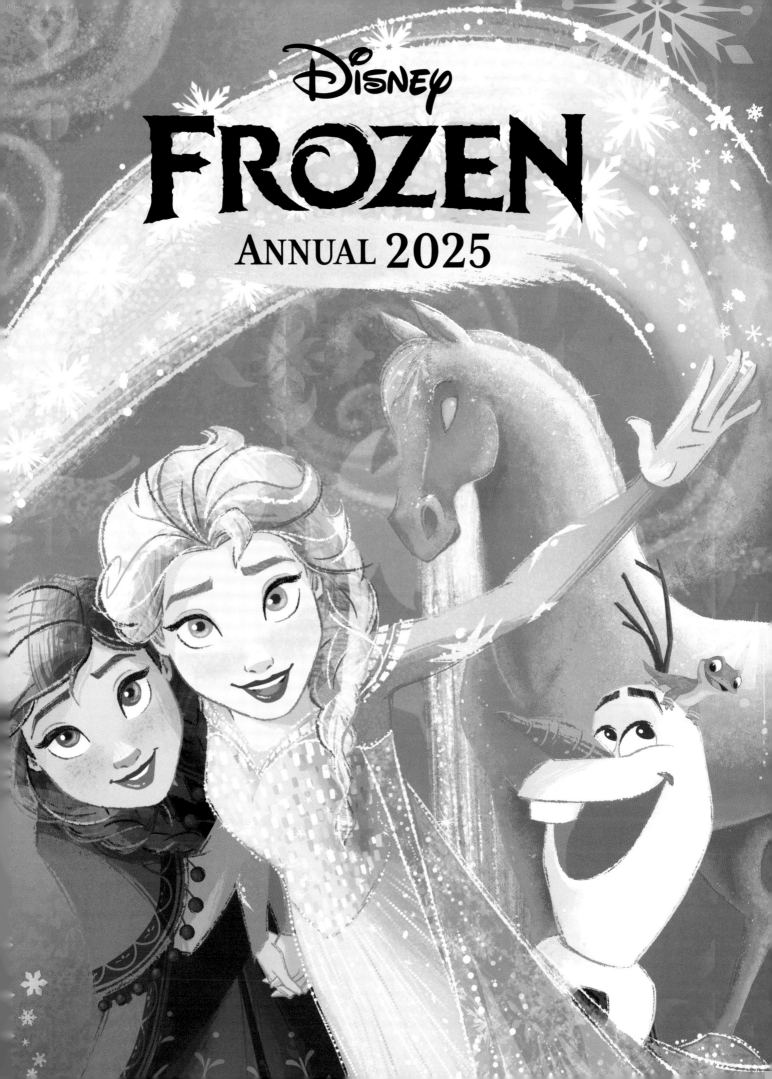

Disney
FROZEN
ANNUAL 2025

Contents

Start Your Journey

Come and meet the Frozen friends before you start your magical journey into the unknown ...

All about *Anna* ...

Always looking on the bright side, Anna brings fun to Arendelle. If only she could keep her sister safe, then she could relaaaax!

Anna is ...

fearless, fun, loyal and a bit clumsy!

Anna loves ...

adventures, parties and her sister, Elsa.

All about *Elsa* ...

With the power to control ice and snow, Elsa has kept her powers hidden from the world. But now she is ready to let it go!

Elsa is ...

brave, quiet, determined.

Elsa loves ...

her family and her freedom.

All about *Kristoff* ...

Brought up in the mountains by trolls, Kristoff is happiest outdoors with his best friend, Sven.

Kristoff is ...

strong, loving and a free spirit.

Kristoff loves ...

reindeer, working as an ice harvester and Anna!

All about *Olaf* ...

This little snowman is always super happy. He may be made of snow, but he wishes it was summer every day!

Olaf is ...
funny, kind, happy!

Olaf loves ...
reading books, his friends and warm hugs.

All about *Sven* ...

This trusty reindeer is always by Kristoff's side. He never strays from danger and will do anything for his best friend.

Sven is ...
brave, loyal and silly!

Sven loves ...
crunchy carrots and helping his friends.

All about *Ryder* ...

Ryder loves his forest home, but he can feel trapped and dreams of exploring beyond the trees.

Ryder is ...
curious, adventurous, friendly.

Ryder loves ...
reindeer (just as much as Kristoff!)

All about *Honeymaren* ...

Honeymaren grew up in the Enchanted Forest. When she meets Elsa, she helps her find the secrets hidden in her home.

Honeymaren is ...
helpful, smart, kind.

Honeymaren loves ...
climbing trees and racing on reindeer.

All about *Yelana* ...

As the leader of the Northuldra, Yelana protects her people from danger.

Yelana is ...
strong, fierce, brave.

Yelana loves ...
the powers of nature.

Making Magic

Elsa is stirring up some special magic today. Add colours to bring the picture to life!

What do you think Elsa is making in the giant pot?

Special Delivery

Anna is sending a letter to Elsa using an easy-breezy delivery!

Study the picture carefully for 30 seconds. Then cover it up with a piece of paper and take the test.

Questions:

1. What colour is Anna's dress?

2. What is swirling in the sky?

3. Are the friends in the Enchanted Forest?

4. How many trees are in the picture?

5. How many buttons does Olaf have?

Answers on page 69.

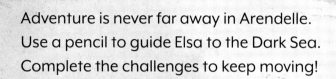

Adventure Starts Here

Adventure is never far away in Arendelle.
Use a pencil to guide Elsa to the Dark Sea.
Complete the challenges to keep moving!

START

Elsa follows
a mysterious voice.
**Sing a song to
guide Elsa on.**

Crystals appear in the sky.
I can count
☐ **crystals.**

Anna catches
up with Elsa.
**Colour her
in to keep
moving.**

Elsa stops to make
an ice sculpture.
Trace it!

12

Watch out! Bruni blasts a fire ball.
Say out loud three words about fire.

A mist surrounds the Enchanted Forest.
Who is hiding in the mist?

....

Yelana tells Elsa about the forest.
Draw leaves on the tree.

Elsa makes it to the Dark Sea.
Trace the wild waves so she can cross the water.

Answers on page 69.

FINISH

A Wonderful Artist

Script: Tea Orsi; Layout: Sara Storino; Characters cleanup: Sara Storino; Backgrounds cleanup: Letizia Algeri; Color: Stefania Santi; Lettering: Arancia Studio; Comics editing: Valentina Cambi

LATER, ANNA TELLS KRISTOFF AND SVEN ABOUT FREYA ...

FREYA IS A TRUE **ARTIST**! I WANT HER TO UNDERSTAND HOW **TALENTED** SHE IS.

I'M SURE YOU ALREADY KNOW HOW TO SHOW HER ...

WELL, I HAVE AN IDEA, BUT ... I NEED **YOUR** HELP!

I'M **ALWAYS** READY TO HELP YOU!

ME TOO!

WHAT SHOULD WE DO?

WE JUST NEED SVEN AND THE **WAGON** ...

WE'RE TAKING FREYA ON A TRIP!

ON A TRIP?!

WHERE?!

YOU'LL FIND OUT SOON!

LATER ...

THIS SHOULD BE FREYA'S HOME!

KNOCK KNOCK

YOUR MAJESTY?!

CALL ME **ANNA**! FREYA, YOU'RE INVITED ON A LITTLE TRIP. WILL YOU COME WITH US? IF YOUR MUM AGREES, OF COURSE ...

SURE, YOUR MAJESTY!

WONDERFUL! LET'S GO!

BACK ABOARD ...

SO, WHERE ARE WE BOUND?

I'M SURE THAT FREYA WANTS TO KNOW, TOO.

WE'RE GOING TO THE **WOODS**!

THIS IS SO EXCITING!

THE WOODS? NOW I'M EVEN MORE **CURIOUS**!

WE JUST NEED TO INVITE SOMEONE SPECIAL, TOO ...

NOW I UNDERSTAND!

THANK YOU, GALE!

THAT **BREEZE** IS OUR FRIEND!

?

SWOOSH

Continued on page 30 ...

Learning is Fun

Books, books, books! Olaf is having so much fun reading about the world today.

Follow the route and write down all the letters you pass to find the answer to Olaf's fun fact.

START

A

S

R

I

U

D

N

D

N

N

A

What makes rainbows?

_ _ _   _ _ _   _ _ _ _ _

Answer on page 69.

Colours of Nature

Ryder and Honeymaren are proud of their wonderful forest home. There are colours, surprises and magic everywhere!

Look at the coloured leaves in the picture. Now take the challenge and count up all the leaves in each colour.

blue ☐

red ☐

yellow ☐

purple ☐

Answers on page 69.

The Power of the Wind

Gale is blowing a breeze through the Enchanted Forest.
Use a pencil to carefully guide Anna along his swirly-whirly trail.

Now colour in all the leaves. Use the key to help you pick colours.

Colour it!
- red
- brown
- green
- orange

← FINISH

↑ START

I coloured in [ ] leaves.

Answer on page 69.

22

A Misty Mission

Anna, Sven and Kristoff need to reach Elsa in the Enchanted Forest, but they can't find a route through the mist.

Which trail will lead the friends to Elsa?
Stay away from the Earth Giants!

PATH 3

PATH 2

PATH 1

FINISH

Answer on page 69.

Family Forever

Crunchy leaves and pumpkin pie ... it's autumn in Arendelle and Anna, Elsa, Olaf, Kristoff and Sven are having a blast!

Can you find five differences in picture 2?

Colour in a pumpkin each time you find a difference.

Answer on page 69.

Warm Hugs

Olaf and Anna love to give warm hugs. Elsa isn't always quite so sure!
Look at each row below and circle the odd picture out.

1   a   b   c   d

2   a   b   c   d

3   a   b   c   d

4   a   b   c   d

Answers on page 69.

Nature Explorers

Honeymaren is giving Olaf a tour of the forest. He is excited to learn all about the creatures he meets on the way.

Join Olaf on his adventure by turning the fingerprints into forest animals and creatures.

Trolls on the Run!

Uh oh, Anna and Kristoff are babysitting the trolls, but they have all run away! Quickly help round up the baby trolls by counting them one by one.

I can count ☐ baby trolls.

Can you spot where Olaf is hiding?

Answers on page 69.

Follow the Lines

It's a big day for Kristoff. He wants to ask Anna to marry him, but he can't find her anywhere. Help Kristoff choose the right path to Anna.

Stay away from Sven and Olaf – Kristoff doesn't want to marry them!

a b c

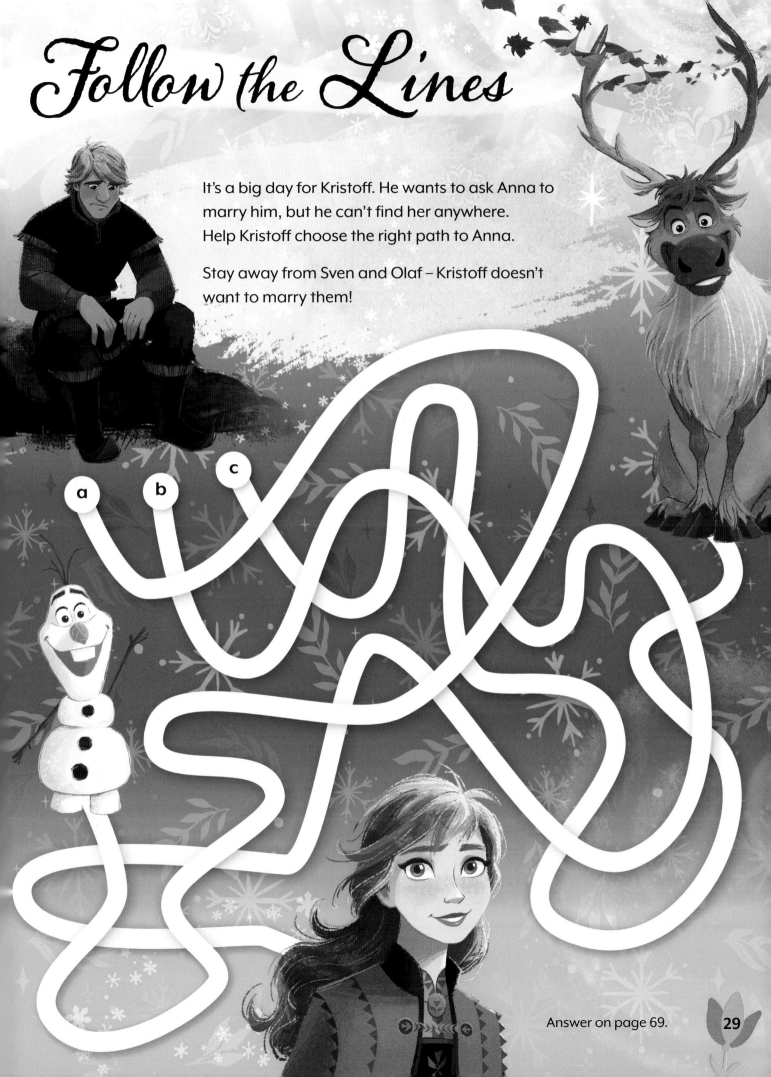

Answer on page 69.

A Wonderful Artist

Script: Tea Orsi; Layout: Sara Storino; Characters cleanup: Sara Storino; Backgrounds cleanup: Letizia Algeri; Color: Stefania Santi; Lettering: Arancia Studio; Comics editing: Valentina Cambi

AFTER A SHORT TRIP ...

HERE WE ARE! DO YOU LIKE IT HERE, FREYA?

WOW, THERE ARE SO MANY COLOURS!

OH YES, THEY'RE SO BRIGHT!

THIS IS VERY INSPIRING, ISN'T IT? DON'T YOU FEEL LIKE MAKING A NEW WREATH? OR MAYBE A PAINTING?

I'D LOVE TO DO THAT, BUT ... MY MUM WON'T BE HAPPY ...

YOU SHOULD DO WHAT MAKES YOU HAPPY, FREYA.

GASP!

OOOH! GALE WAS FAST!

QUEEN ELSA?!

ANNA INVITED ME ON YOUR TRIP, AND I COULDN'T MISS IT!

I KNEW YOU WOULD COME!

ANNA TOLD ME THAT YOU'RE AN AMAZING ARTIST, FREYA. I REALLY WANTED TO MEET YOU!

AN ARTIST?

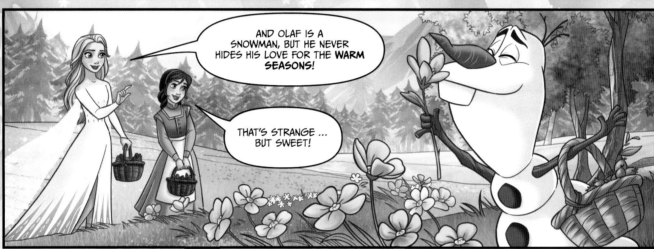

The End

35

Be Creative!

Now you have read the story 'A Wonderful Artist', can you show Elsa your unique ideas?

Use crayons to decorate this wreath. You could doodle flowers, crystals, berries, leaves ... anything you like!

Magic Match

Magic in the Dark Sea is strong and powerful.

Use your own powers to find the matching pair of Elsa and the Water Nokk.

Did you know?
Nokk is the spirit of water.

Answers on page 69.

Party Time

Help Anna round up all the guests for a winter party at the castle. Can you find three-in-row of each guest across or up and down?

Which friend appears the most times in the grid?

Now draw three things you would take to Anna's winter party!

Answers on page 69.

Believe in the Journey

When a mysterious voice calls to Elsa, she gets ready for a mission into the unknown.

Guide Elsa to the forest, meeting new friends along the way.

START

FINISH

Answers on page 69.

A Secret Recipe

Original story by Erica David; Manuscript adaptation by Chantal Pericoli; Layout: Gianluca Barone; Cleanup: Letizia Algeri; Color: Dario Calabria; Lettering: Arancia Studio; Comics editing: Valentina Cambi

IT'S A GLORIOUS MORNING IN ARENDELLE ...

ELSA, AREN'T YOU EXCITED? TODAY IS THE DAY OF FLANGENDORFERS!

FLANGEN ... WHAT?

THE FLANGENDORFERS!

I'VE NEVER HEARD OF A "FLANGENDORFER."

YOU MEAN YOU'VE NEVER TASTED ONE? I HEAR THEY'RE THE MOST DELICIOUS DESSERT IN ALL OF ARENDELLE! AND WE'RE GOING TO DISCOVER THEIR SECRET RECIPE.

BUT ... I HAVE WORK TO DO.

DISCOVERING THE BIG SECRETS OF YOUR KINGDOM IS WORK.

OK, ONE FLANGENDORFER WON'T HURT!

MY QUEEN, ALLOW ME TO INTRODUCE MYSELF ...

CHEF FLORIAN, AT YOUR SERVICE.

!

NICE TO MEET YOU!

SNAP

MAY I PRESENT TO YOU THE FINEST DESSERT IN ALL OF ARENDELLE!

WOW!

CHEF FLORIAN, YOU'RE A GENIUS!

LATER...

WHO WANTS SECONDS?

THAT WAS WONDERFUL. BUT I DON'T THINK I COULD EAT ANOTHER BITE.

COME WITH ME, THEN. I'LL SHOW YOU THE SECRETS OF THE FLANGENDORFER.

MY FAMILY HAS BEEN MAKING FLANGENDORFERS FOR YEARS. THE DESSERT WAS INVENTED BY MY GREAT-GREAT-GREAT-GREAT-GREAT-UNCLE A LONG TIME AGO.

THIS IS OUR SPECIAL FLANGENDORFER DOUGH. I WILL TEACH YOU HOW TO ROLL IT FLAT.

HUMPH!

SORRY, ANNA. THIS BIG MESS IS ALL MY FAULT.

MMMPH!

I THINK WE SHOULD APOLOGISE TO FLORIAN.

MMMPH!

I KNOW YOU'RE UPSET, BUT WON'T YOU AT LEAST SAY SOMETHING?

MMMPH!

OH, YOUR LIPS! THEY'RE SEALED SHUT FROM THAT BATTER!

WELL, AT LEAST YOU WON'T REVEAL CHEF FLORIAN'S SECRET RECIPE! HAHAHA!

The End

Let's Draw!

Learn to draw your very own Olaf. Use a pencil to trace over the lines to draw Olaf in the box opposite.

Add letters in the empty grid to show Olaf in the correct order. The first letter has been done for you.

Do you want to draw Olaf all mixed up again?

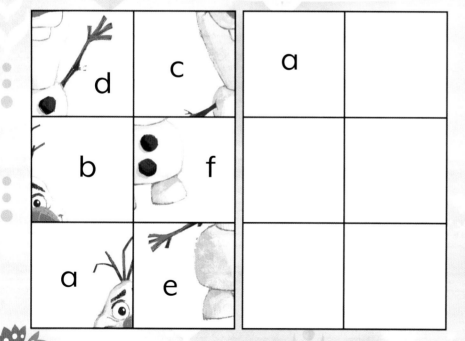

Snowy Squares

It's time to battle it out in a game of Snowy Squares!

SCORES

Player 1

Player 2

How to play:

- Grab a friend to play the game with. Take turns to connect two dots to make a line.
- If you connect two dots to complete a box, write the first letter of your name in the square and score one point.
- If you connect a square with a Frozen friend inside, you win 2 points.
- When all boxes are filled, add up your points to see who won.

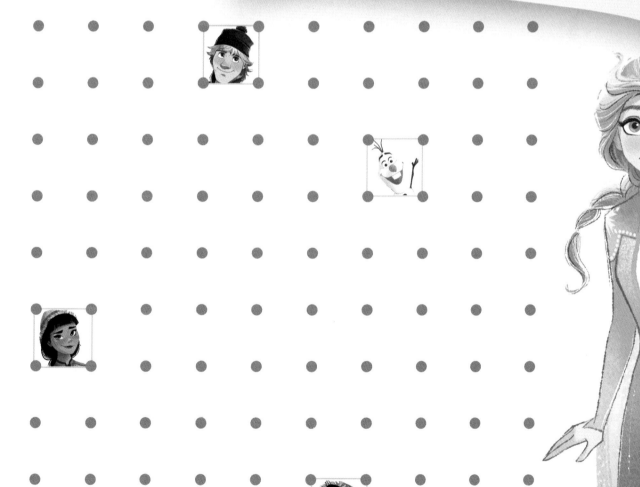

47

Discover Nature

Imagine you have just entered
the mysterious and misty
Enchanted Forest with Elsa.
It is full of magic and surprise.
Draw what you see!

Find Your Magic!

A New Adventure

There's a whole new world for Anna and Elsa to explore together. Grab your crayons and fill the picture with colour.

Tick the things the sisters might need for an adventure. Cross the things they won't need!

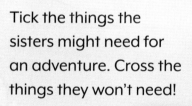

Adventure Checklist

map ☐

tiger ☐

water ☐

rubber duck ☐

bag ☐

Answers on page 69.

Kristoff's Icy Lesson

ONE DAY, IN ARENDELLE ...

GOOD MORNING, CHILDREN!

Manuscript: Tea Orsi; layout: Alberto Zanon; cleanup: Letizia Algeri; color: MichelAngela World; lettering: Arancia Studio; comics editing: Valentina Cambi

GOOD MORNING, QUEEN ELSA!

GOOD MORNING, PRINCESS ANNA!

AS YOU ALL KNOW, TODAY KRISTOFF WILL TALK ABOUT HIS JOB AS ICE HARVESTER ...

GOOD MORNING, EVERYONE! ARE YOU READY FOR SOME ICE LEARNING?

TOUGH CROWD, HUH?

DON'T WORRY. THEY JUST NEED TO WARM UP. THEY'RE GONNA LOVE YOU!

LET'S START WITH THE BASICS, OK?

ICE HARVESTING IS A SCIENCE THAT REQUIRES SKILL AND A DEEP KNOWLEDGE OF ...

EXCUSE ME, SIR!

YES?

HAVE YOU EVER CUT AN ICE BLOCK THIS BIG?

WHAT ABOUT ONE AS BIG AS A REINDEER?

HOW ABOUT AS BIG AS A SAUNA?

AND AS BIG AS A CASTLE?

WAIT, WAIT!

ICE HARVESTING IS HARD WORK ... I'M GOING TO TELL YOU HOW IT'S DONE AND ...

CAN WE SEE THE BIG ICE BLOCKS INSTEAD?

DID YOU BRING THEM?

HOW BIG IS YOUR SLEIGH?

SWISHHH

The End

57

Wonderful Words

Anna and her friends are all unique and different, and that's what makes them special.

Trace over the words with a pencil. Then draw a line to match each word to a friend.

Pabbie

Anna

Olaf

Sven

Answers on page 69.

A Messy Mystery

Whoops! Somebody knocked over Elsa's birthday cake and made a big mess at the palace. Who can it be?

Solve the clues to find out!

Clues

1. They are smiling.
2. They are not a human.
3. They are not made of snow.
4. They have brown eyes.

Sven

Kristoff

Anna

Bruni

Olaf

Answer on page 69.

Take the Test

Can you answer these questions about our friends from Arendelle and The Enchanted Forest?

1 Circle the **smallest** friend.

 a
 b
 c
 d

2 Circle the **tallest** friend.

 a
 b
 c
 d

3 Circle the **fastest** friend.

 a
 b
 c
 d

4 Circle the **furry** friend.

 a
 b
 c
 d

Answers on page 69.

Thank You

Olaf thinks making "thank you" postcards for his friends is so cool! Why not say "thank you" to somebody in your world too?

What to Do ...

· Grab your best pencils and colour in the postcard.

· Ask a grown-up to use scissors to cut around the dotted lines.

· Write a message and draw something special on the back.

· Now deliver it to whoever you want to thank. It will make their day!

A N-ice **BIG** Thank You

to ....

© Disney

Thank You
for

....
....
....
....

from

....

Jigsaw Fun

With her magic and kindness, Elsa has brought together the Nature Spirits and the people of Northuldra and Arendelle.

Draw letters to match the missing pieces to the jigsaw picture.

a

b

c

d

Answers on page 69.

Tick, Tock, Around the Clock

Trace the times on the clocks as you whizz through Anna's day. From fun gifts to magical trips, get ready for a day of frosty fun!

8 o'clock

Wake-up, Anna!
Draw some breakfast to start the day.

Snow Day!

I count ⬜ snowballs.

10 o'clock

Answer on page 69.

Take a trip to see Elsa in the Enchanted Forest.

Colour the crystals in frosty colours.

1 o'clock

Surprise Kristoff with a fun gift!

Draw a present in the box.

5 o'clock

What a busy day! It's time for bed.

Tell Olaf a goodnight story.

7 o'clock

The Big Frozen Quiz

How much do you know about the Frozen world? Put your knowledge to the test in this super-fun fan quiz!

1

Where does Anna live?

a) Arendelle

b) The North Mountain

c) The Enchanted Forest

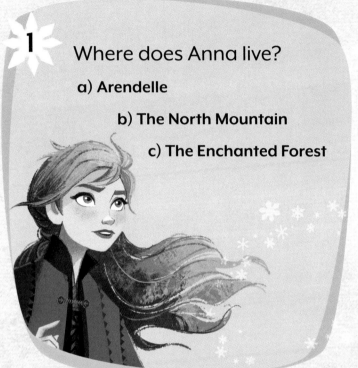

2

What is Sven?

a) a horse

b) a reindeer

c) a bull

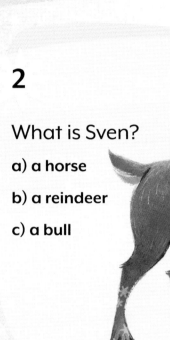

3

What does Elsa keep hidden for years?

a) her magic powers

b) her books

c) her crown

4

Who was Kristoff brought up by?

a) Yelana

b) the trolls

c) Elsa

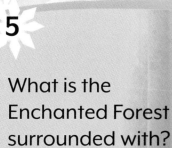

5

What is the Enchanted Forest surrounded with?

a) rainbows

b) snow

c) mist

6

What is Bruni's power?

a) storms

b) fire

c) water

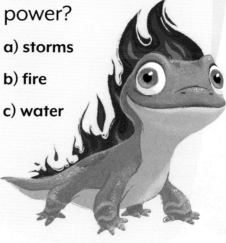

7

What does Water Nokk help Elsa cross?

a) The Rumbling River

b) The Snowy Mountain

c) The Dark Sea

8

Who loves hugs the most in Arendelle?

a) Yelana

b) Olaf

c) Grand Pabbie

9

Who does Kristoff want to marry?

a) Anna

b) Yelana

c) Earth Giant

10

Who is the Snow Queen?

a) Honeymaren

b) Anna

c) Elsa

Answers on page 69.

Stronger Together

Anything is possible when the friends
stick together! Colour them in.

Answers

Page 11 Special Delivery

1. green
2. leaves
3. No
4. 2
5. 3

Page 12 Adventure Starts Here

I can count 10 crystals.
Olaf is hiding in the mist.

Page 20 Learning is Fun

Sun and rain make rainbows.

Page 21 Colours of Nature

blue = 7   red = 5
yellow = 8   purple = 6

Page 22
The Power of the Wind

There are 10 leaves.

Page 23 A Misty Mission

Path 2 leads to Elsa.

Page 24-25 Family Forever

Page 26 Warm Hugs

1 — b, 2 — d, 3 — a, 4 — c.

Page 28 Trolls on the Run!

There are 15 baby trolls.

Page 29 Follow the Lines

Path b takes Kristoff to Anna.

Page 37 Magic Match

Pictures 1 and 5 are
a matching pair.

Page 38 Party Time

Honeymaren appears the most.

Page 39
Believe in the Journey

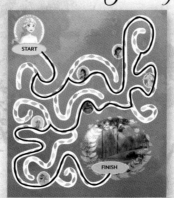

Page 46 Let's Draw!

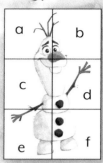

Page 51 A New Adventure

The sisters might need a map, water
and a bag on their adventure.

Page 58 Wonderful Words

You could match the words and
names as follows, other choices
are fine too!

funny — Olaf   wise — Pabbie
strong — Sven   brave — Anna

Page 59 A Messy Mystery

Sven made the mess.

Page 60 Take the Test

1 — b, 2 — c, 3 — b, 4 — c.

Page 63 Jigsaw Fun

Page 64-65
Tick, Tock, Around the Clock

There are 5 snowballs.

Page 66-67
The Big Frozen Quiz

1. a	2. b	3. a
4. b	5. c	6. b
7. c	8. b	9. a
10. c